THE NEW COMPOSERS PIANO

LUDOVICO EINAUDI • MICHAEL NYMAN • GIOVANNI ALLEVI
YANN TIERSEN • JOHN WILLIAMS • ENNIO MORRICONE
ASTOR PIAZZOLLA • RYUICHI SAKAMOTO • JAMES HORNER
YIRUMA • NICOLA PIOVANI • JOHN BARRY • ELTON JOHN

VOLONTÈ&Co

Foto in copertina: © iaremenko - Fotolia.com

CONTENTS

BACK TO LIFE

Music by Giovanni Allevi

COME SEI VERAMENTE

Music by Giovanni Allevi

COMPTINE D'UN AUTRE ÉTÉ

(from *Le Fabuleux Destin d'Amélie Poulain a/k/a Amélie*)

Music by Yann Tiersen

20

GIÙ LA TESTA

(from *Giù la testa* a/k/a *Duck, You Sucker!* a/k/a *A Fistful of Dynamite*
a/k/a *Once Upon a Time… the Revolution*)

Music by Ennio Morricone

Moderato

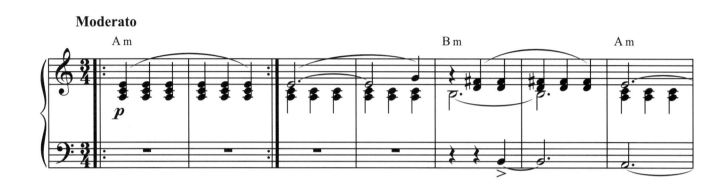

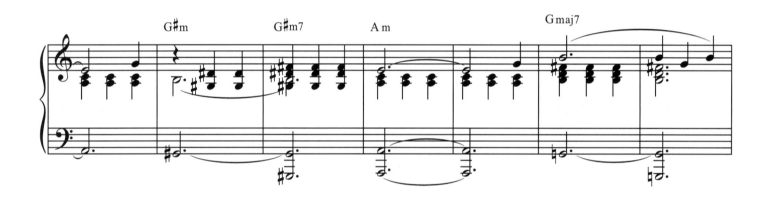

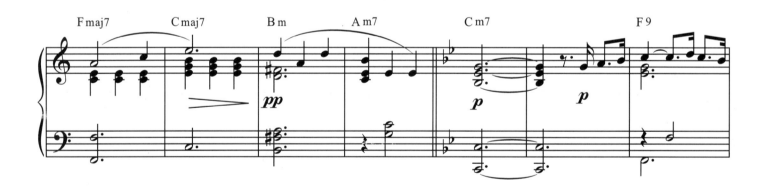

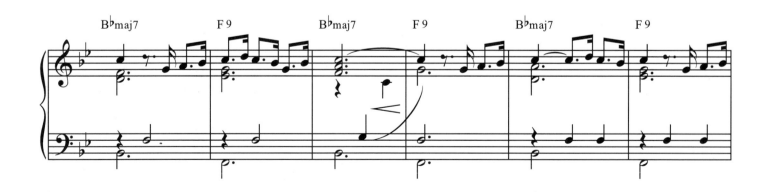

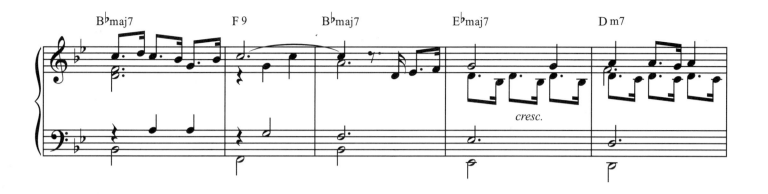

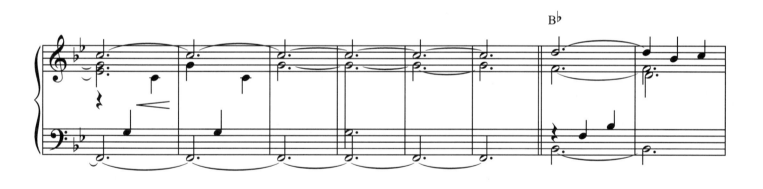

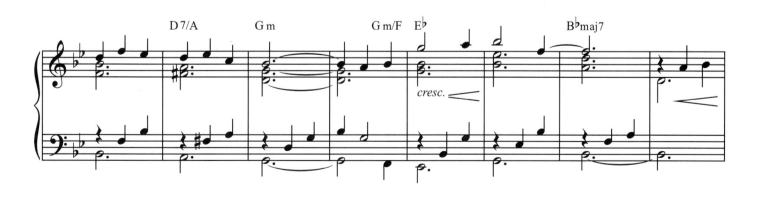

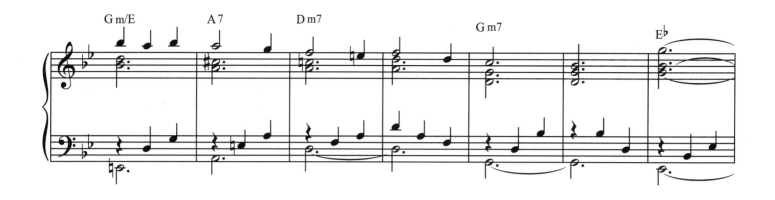

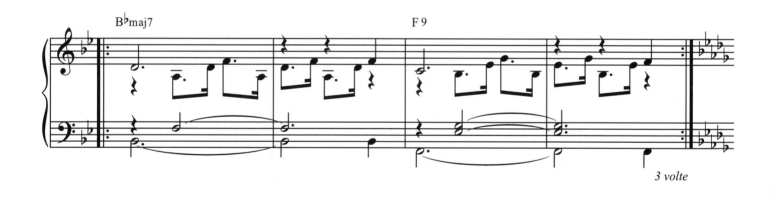

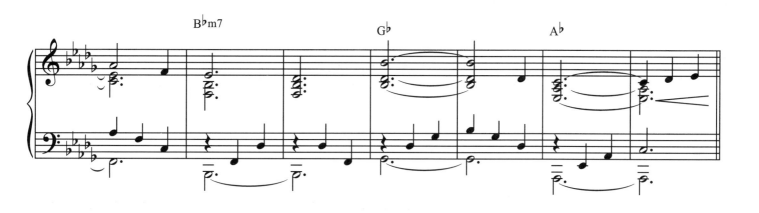

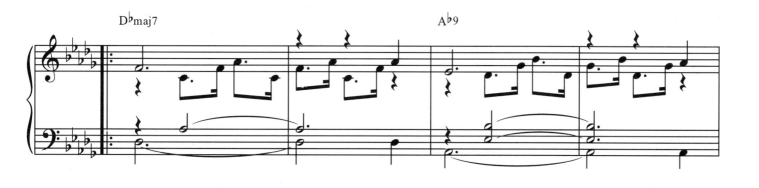

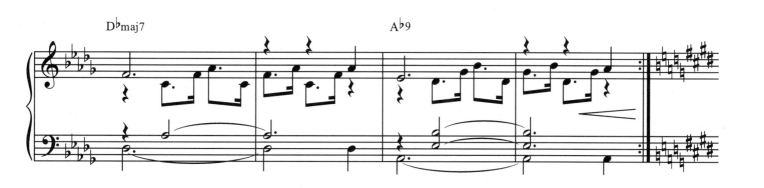

26

HEDWIG'S THEME

(from *Harry Potter and the Sorcerer's Stone*)

Music by John Williams

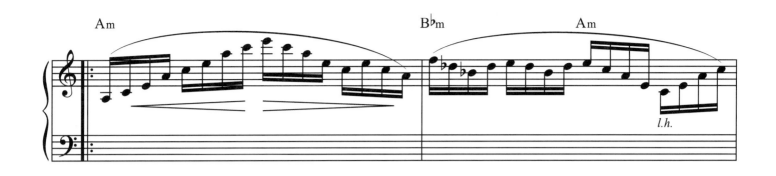

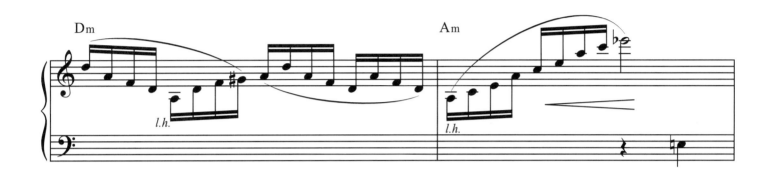

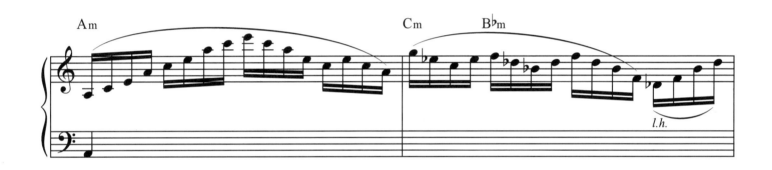

LA VALSE D'AMÉLIE

(from *Le Fabuleux Destin d'Amélie Poulain a/k/a Amélie*)

Music by Yann Tiersen

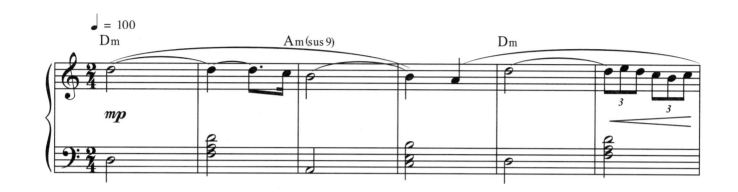

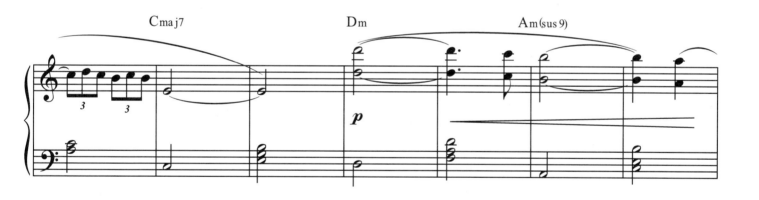

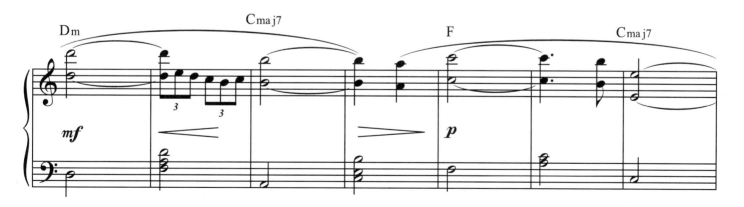

I GIORNI

Music by Ludovico Einaudi

LA VITA È BELLA

(from *La vita è bella* a/k/a *Life is Beautiful*)

Music by Nicola Piovani

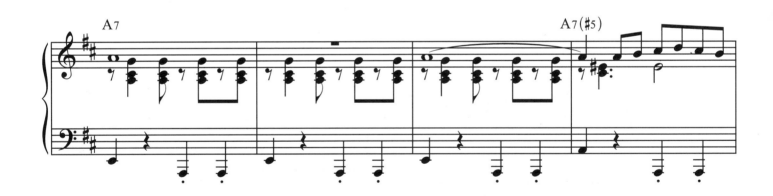

© 1997 Tentacoli Edizioni Musicali Srl – Via Icilio 9 – Roma
Tutti i diritti sono riservati a termini di legge per tutti i paesi del mondo.
All Rights Reserved. International Copyright Secured.

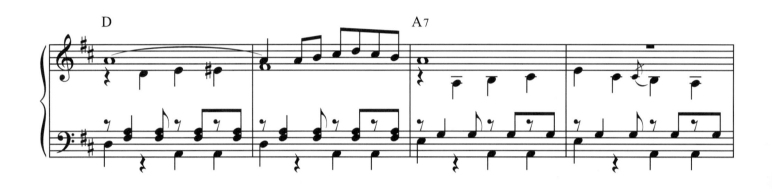

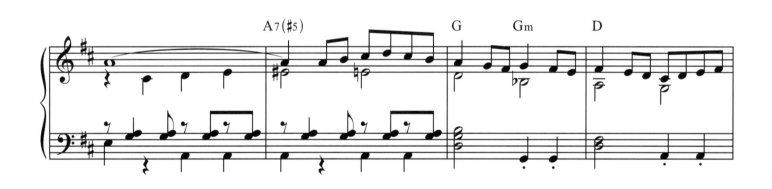

ROSE

(ROSE'S THEME from *Titanic*)

Music by James Horner

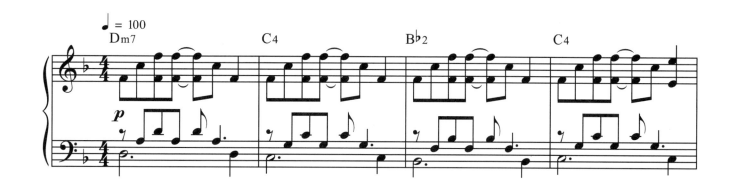

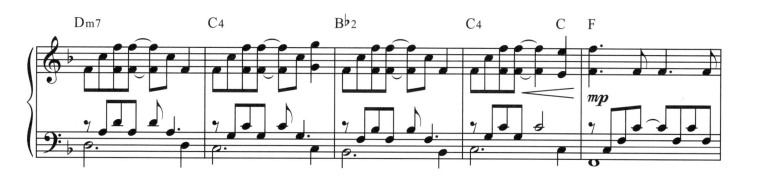

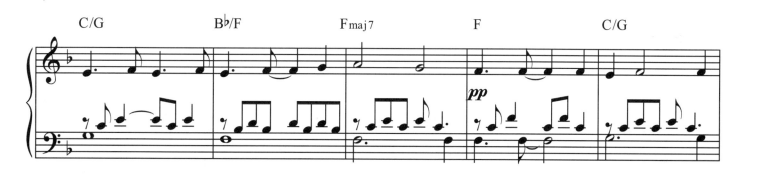

49

50

LIBERTANGO

Music by Astor Piazzolla

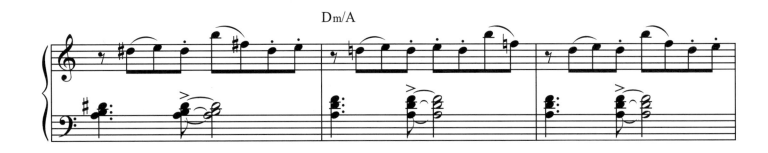

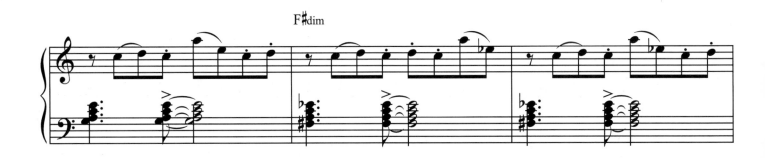

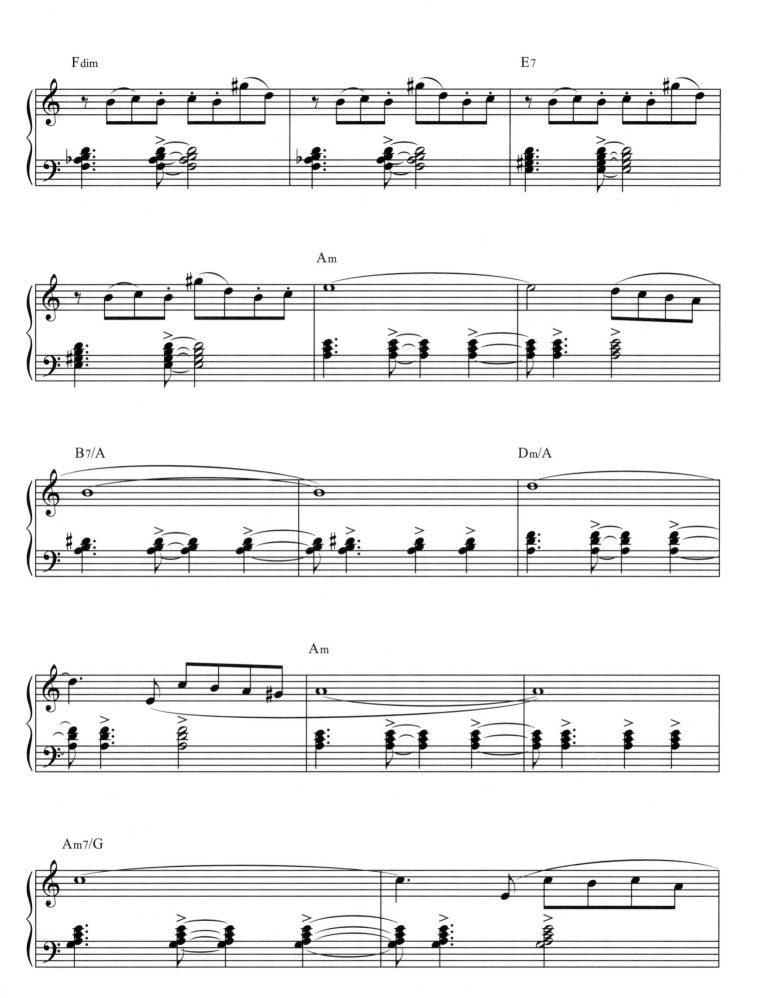

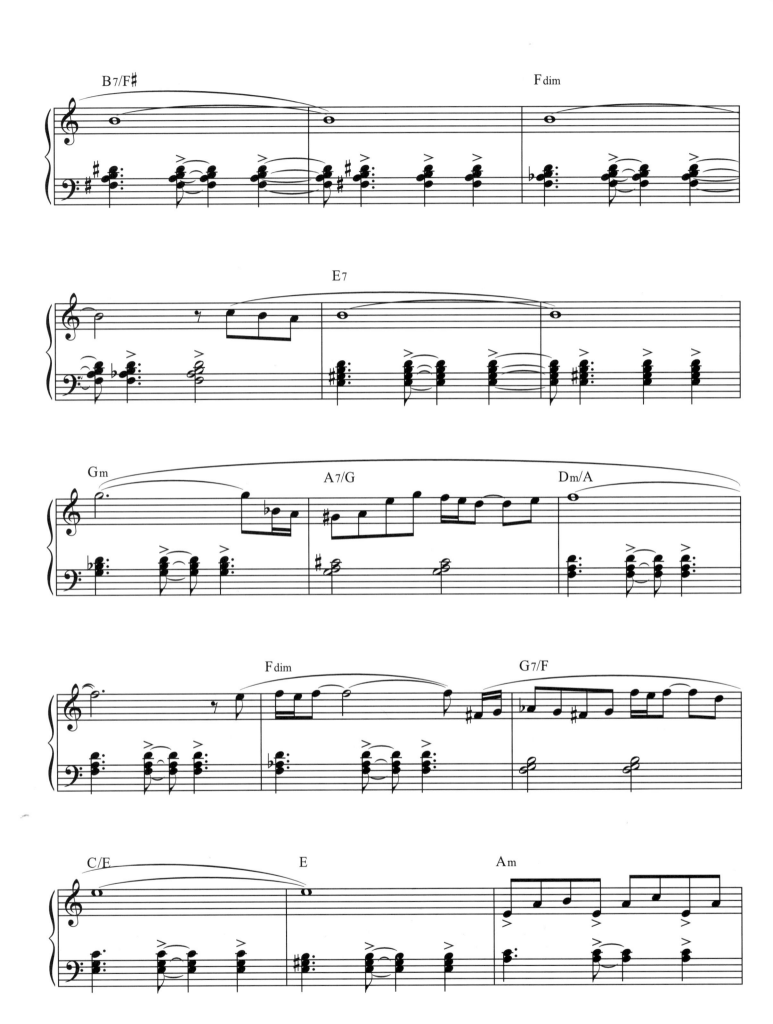

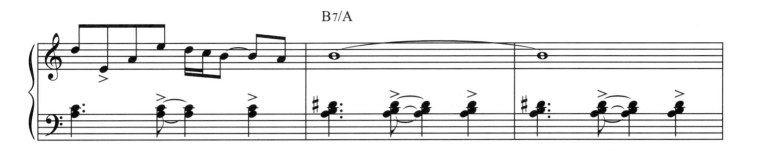

Repeat and fade

MERRY CHRISTMAS MR. LAWRENCE

(from *Merry Christmas, Mr. Lawrence* a/k/a *Furyo*)

Music by Ryuichi Sakamoto

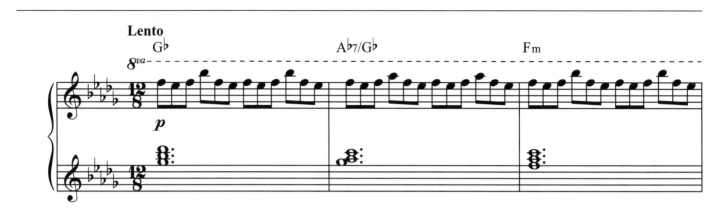

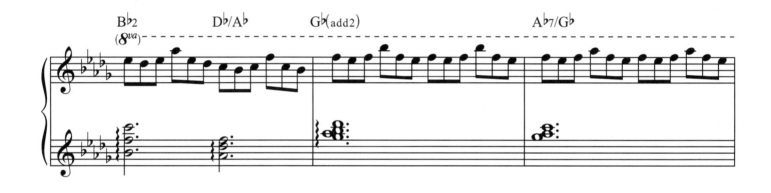

NUOVO CINEMA PARADISO

(from *Nuovo Cinema Paradiso a/k/a Cinema Paradiso*)

Music by Andrea Morricone - Ennio Morricone

Andante Moderato

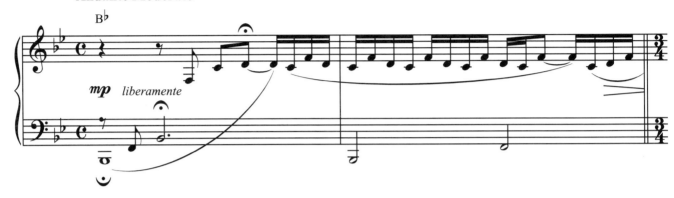

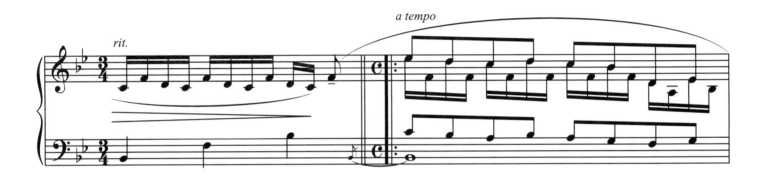

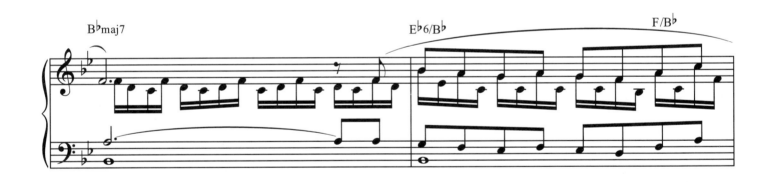

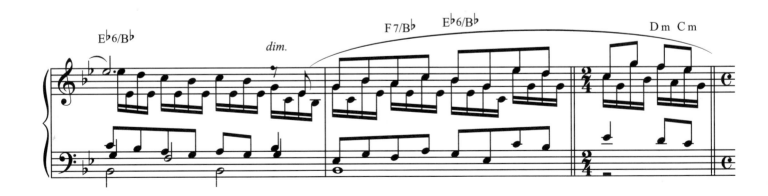

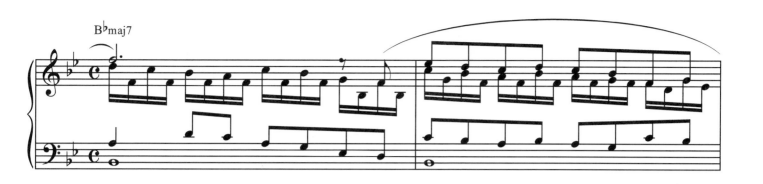

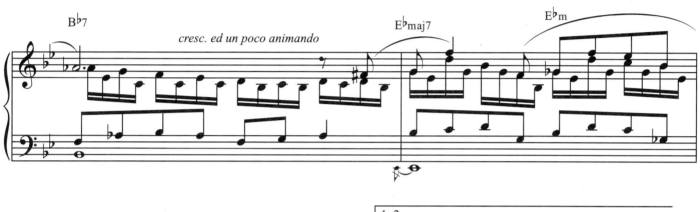

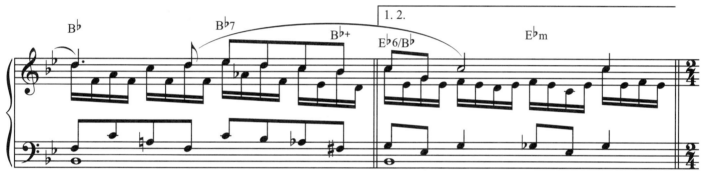

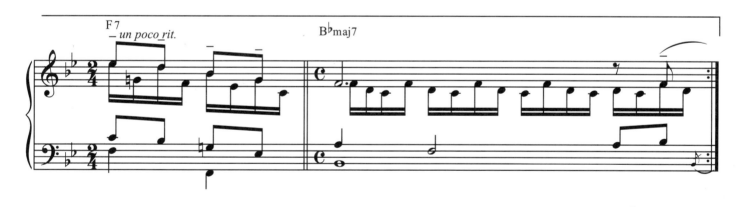

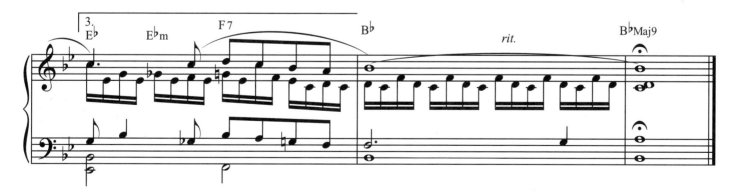

NUVOLE BIANCHE

Music by Ludovico Einaudi

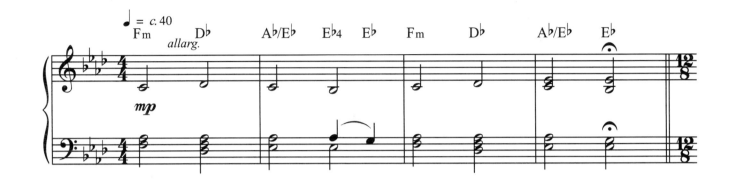

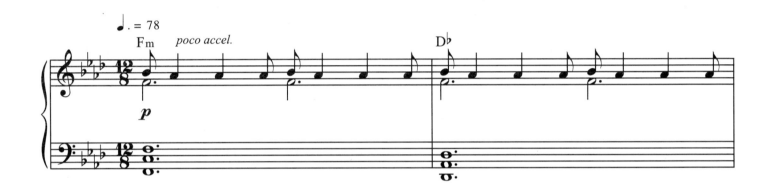

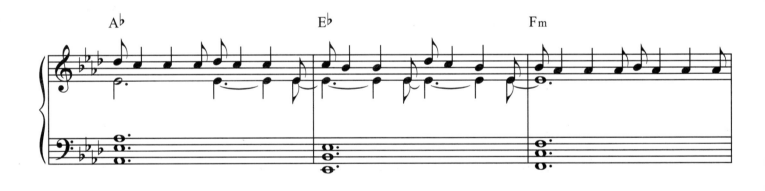

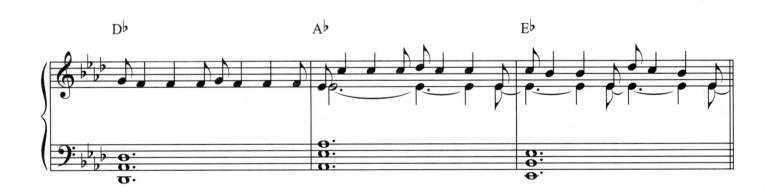

70

RIVER FLOWS IN YOU

Music by Yiruma

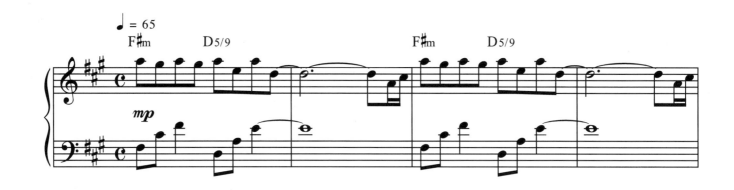

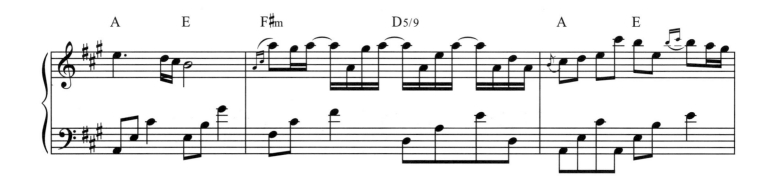

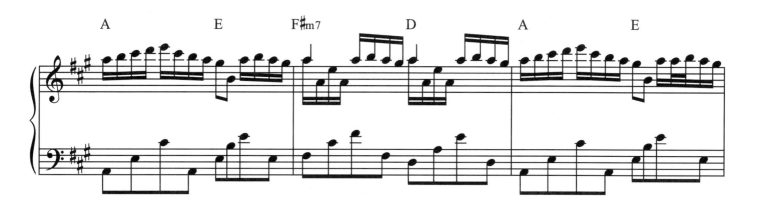

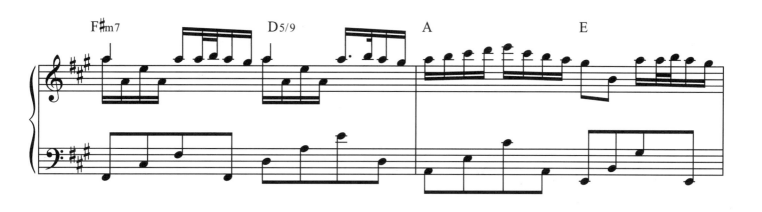

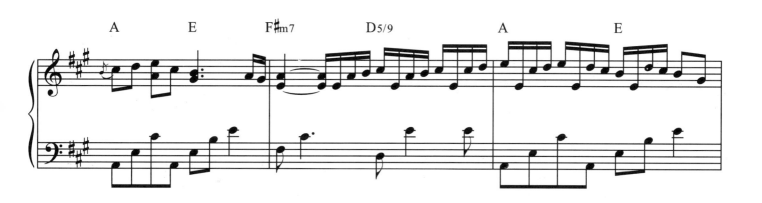

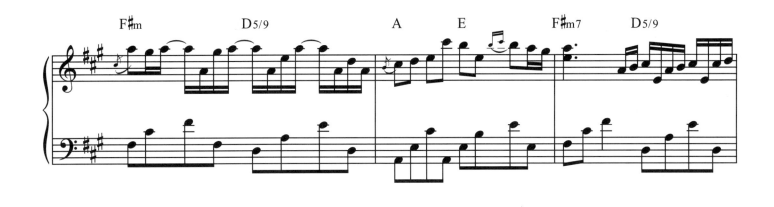

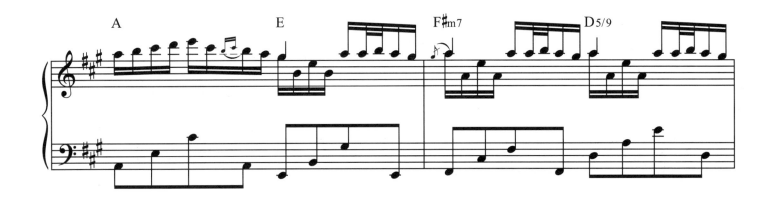
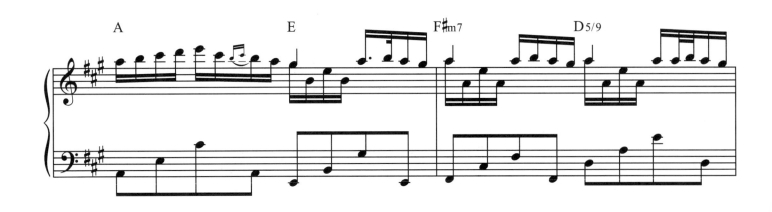

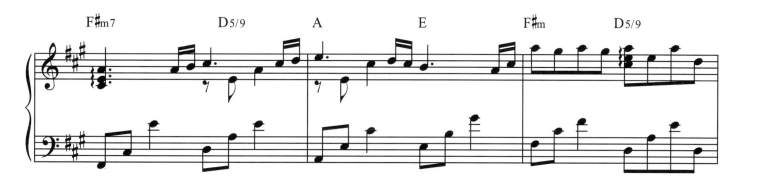

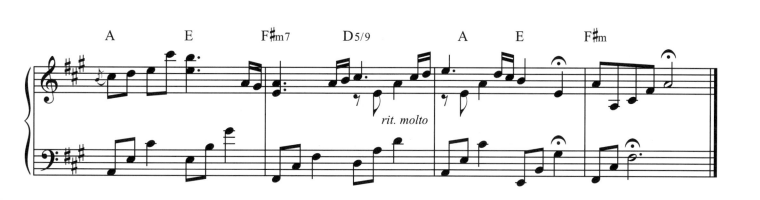

SONG FOR GUY

Music by Elton John

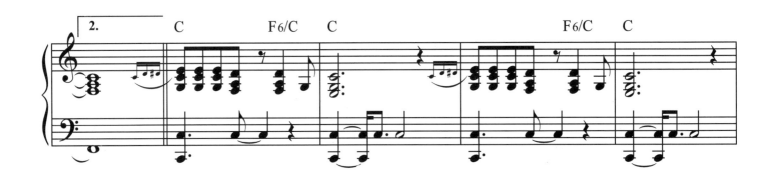

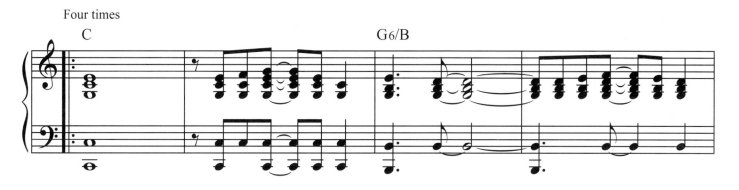

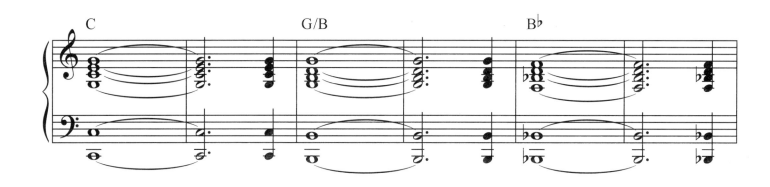

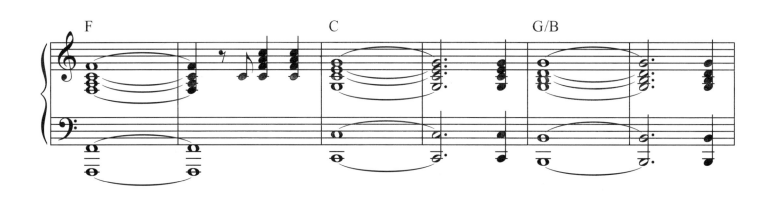

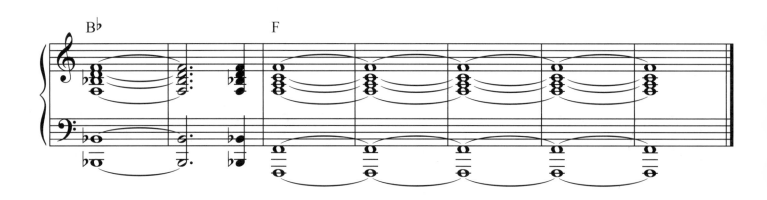

THE HEART ASKS PLEASURE FIRST

(THE PROMISE / THE SACRIFICE from *The Piano*)

Music by Michael Nyman

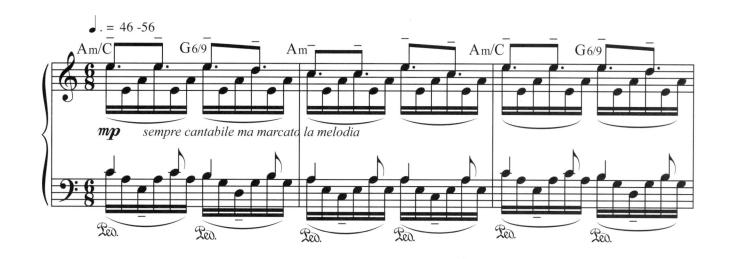

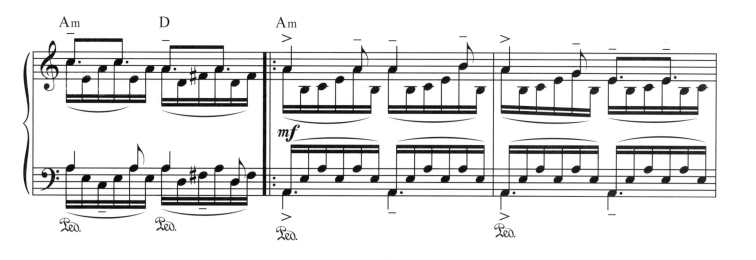

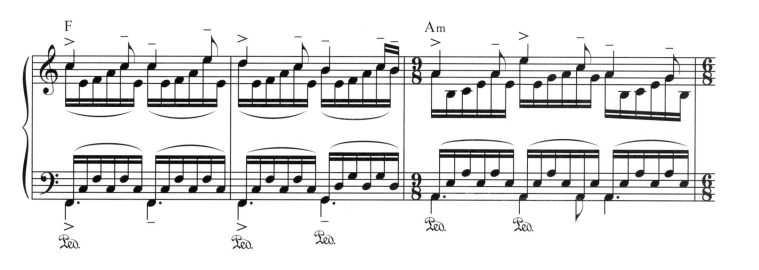

85

THE PERSUADERS

(MAIN THEME from *The Persuaders!*)

Music by John Barry

Moderately, with intensity

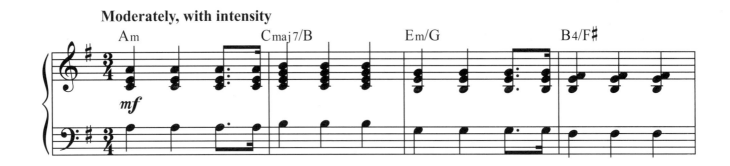

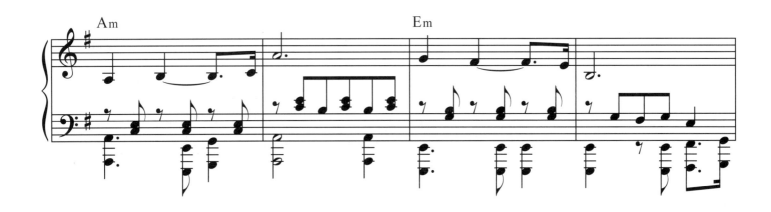

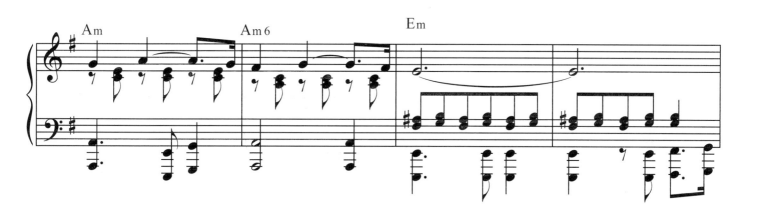

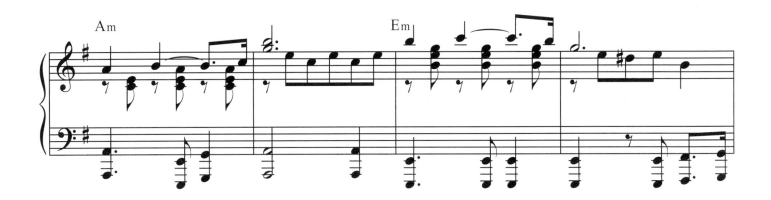

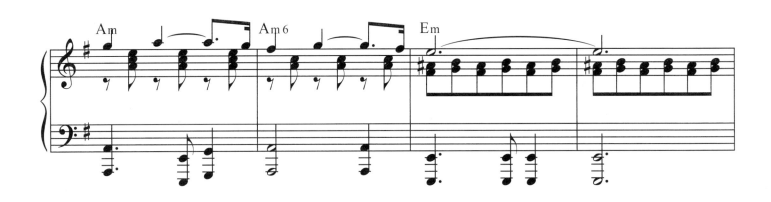

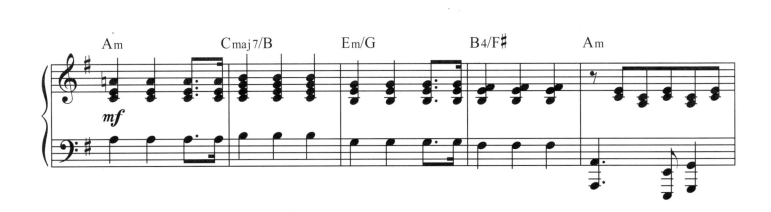

UNA MATTINA

(from *Quasi amici a/k/a Intouchables*)

Music by Ludovico Einaudi

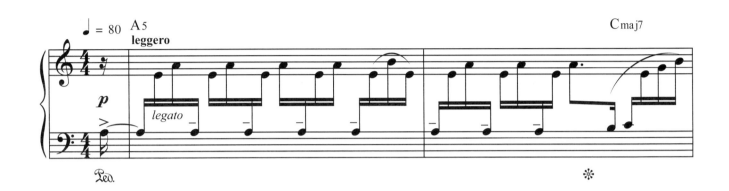

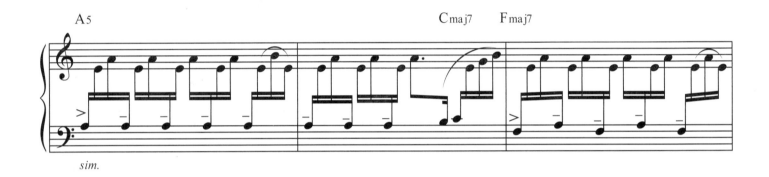

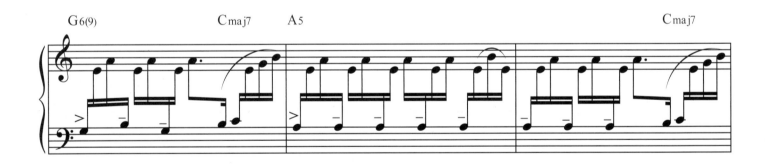

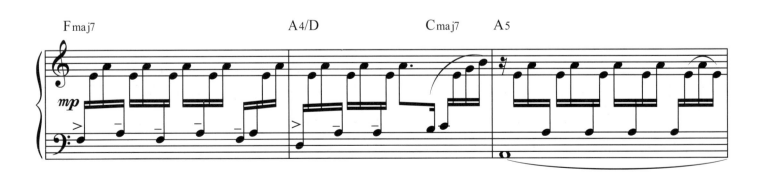

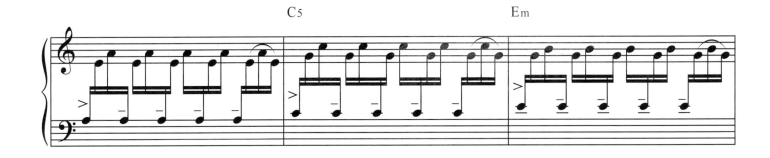

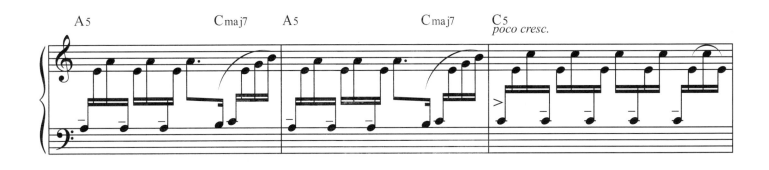

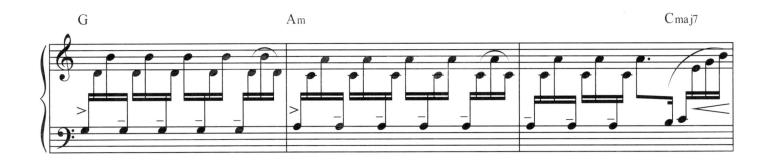

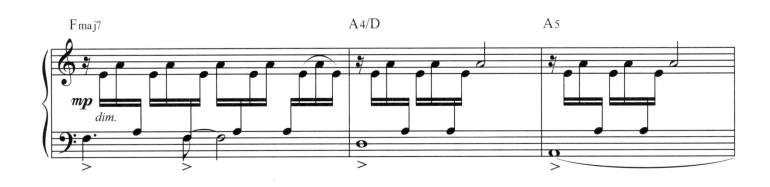

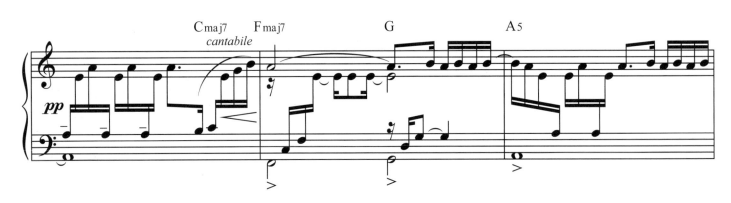

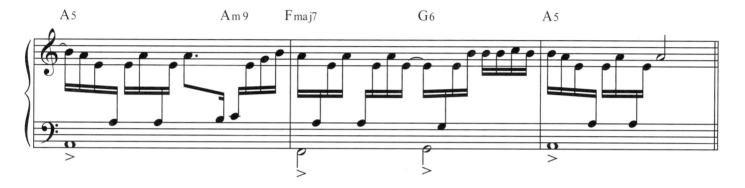

INGRAF s.r.l. - Via Monte S. Genesio 7 - Milano
Stampato in Italia - Printed in Italy - Imprimé en Italie 2020